TRINITY
COLLEGE LONDON

THE EXAM AT A GLANCE

For your Rock & Pop exam you will need to perform a set of **three songs** and one of the **Session skills** assessments, either **Playback** or **Improvising**. You can choose the order in which you play your set-list.

Song 1

Choose a song from this book

OR from www.trinityrock.com

Song 2

Choose a different song from this book

OR from www.trinityrock.com

OR perform a song you have chosen yourself: this could be your own cover version or a song you have written. It should be at the same level as the songs in this book. See the website for detailed requirements.

Song 3: Technical focus

Choose one of the Technical focus songs from this book, which cover three specific technical elements.

Session skills

Choose either **Playback** or **Improvising**.

When you are preparing for your exam please check on **www.trinityrock.com** for the most up-to-date information and requirements as these can change from time to time.

CONTENTS

Tuning track: E, A, D, G, B, E with a pause between each note.

Trinity College London's Rock & Pop syllabus and supporting publications have been devised and produced in association with Faber Music and Peters Edition London.

Trinity College London
Registered office:
89 Albert Embankment
London SE1 7TP UK
T + 44 (0)20 7820 6100
F + 44 (0)20 7820 6161
E music@trinitycollege.co.uk
www.trinitycollege.co.uk

Registered in the UK. Company no. 02683033
Charity no. 1014792
Patron HRH The Duke of Kent KG

Copyright © 2012 Trinity College London
Second impression, March 2013

Cover and book design by Chloë Alexander
Brand development by Andy Ashburner @ Caffeinehit (www.caffeinehit.com)
Photographs courtesy of Rex Features Limited.
Printed in England by Caligraving Ltd

Audio produced, mixed and mastered by Tom Fleming
Guitar arranged by Tom Fleming
Backing tracks arranged by Tom Fleming
Musicians
Vocals: Bo Walton, Brendan Reilly & Alison Symons
Keyboards: Oliver Weeks
Guitar: Tom Fleming
Bass: Ben Hillyard
Drums: George Double
Studio Engineer: Joel Davies www.thelimehouse.com

ISBN: 978-0-85736-219-3

SONGS

I'M GONNA BE (500 MILES)

The Proclaimers
Words and Music by Charles Reid and Craig Reid

SONGS

SHEENA IS A PUNK ROCKER

Ramones

Words and Music by Thomas Erdelyi, John Cummings, Jeffrey Hyman and Douglas Calvin

♩ = 160 **Punk Rock** *2 bars count-in*

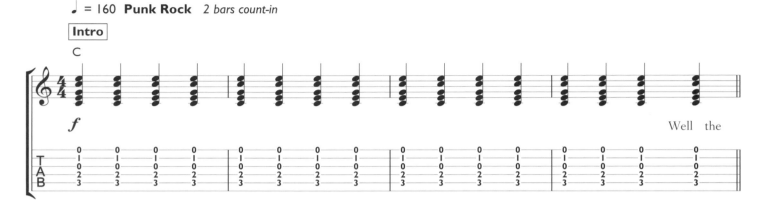

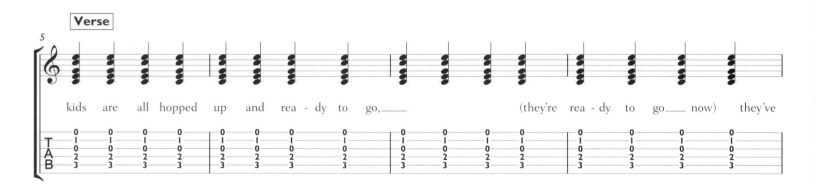

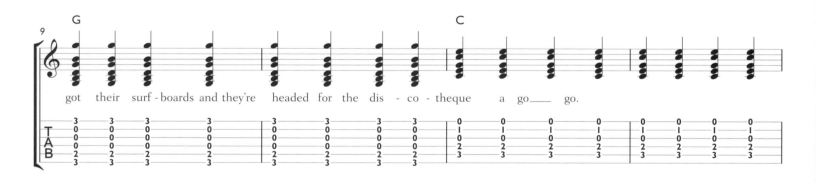

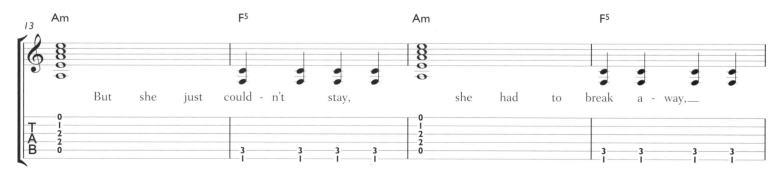

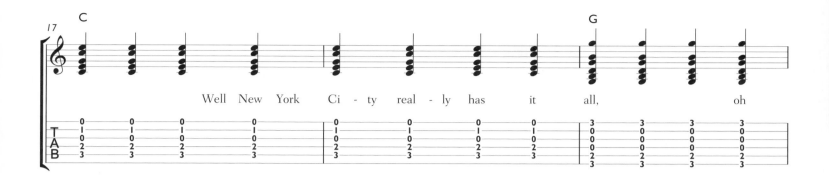

Well New York Ci - ty real - ly has it all,   oh

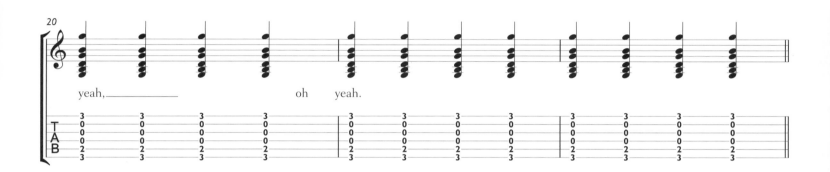

yeah,_____   oh yeah.

Chorus

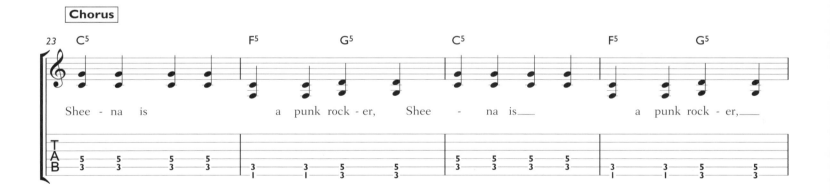

Shee - na is   a punk rock - er, Shee - na is____   a punk rock - er,____

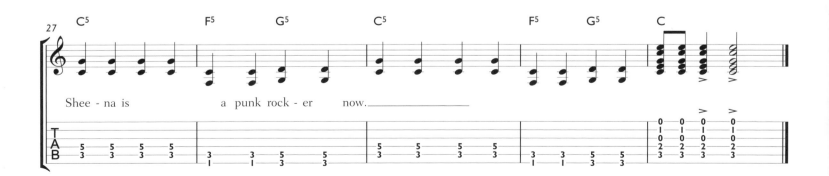

Shee - na is   a punk rock - er   now._____

SONGS

THESE BOOTS ARE MADE FOR WALKIN'

Nancy Sinatra
Written by Lee Hazlewood

♩ = 84 **Pop** *2 bars count-in*

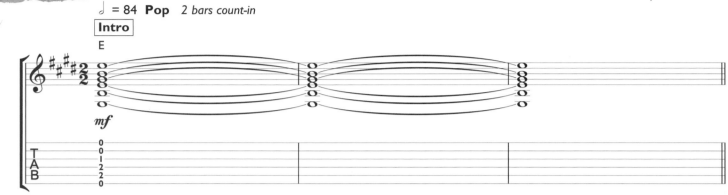

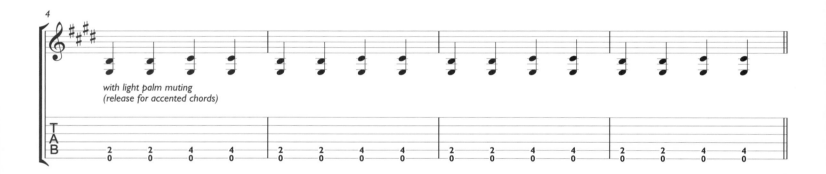

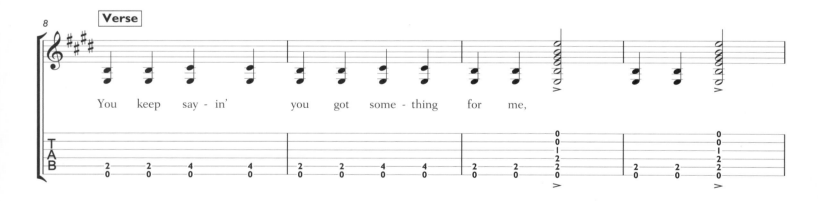

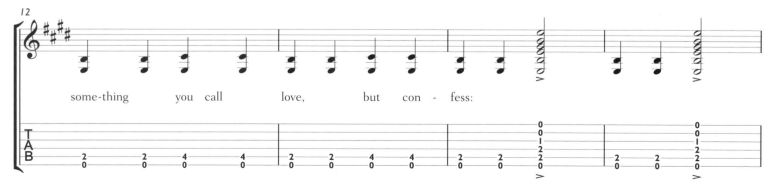

Lyrics: You keep say-in' you got some-thing for me, some-thing you call love, but con-fess:

© 1965-66 ® 1993 Criterion Music Corporation • Used by Permission
All Rights Reserved • International Copyright Secured.

www.trinityrock.com

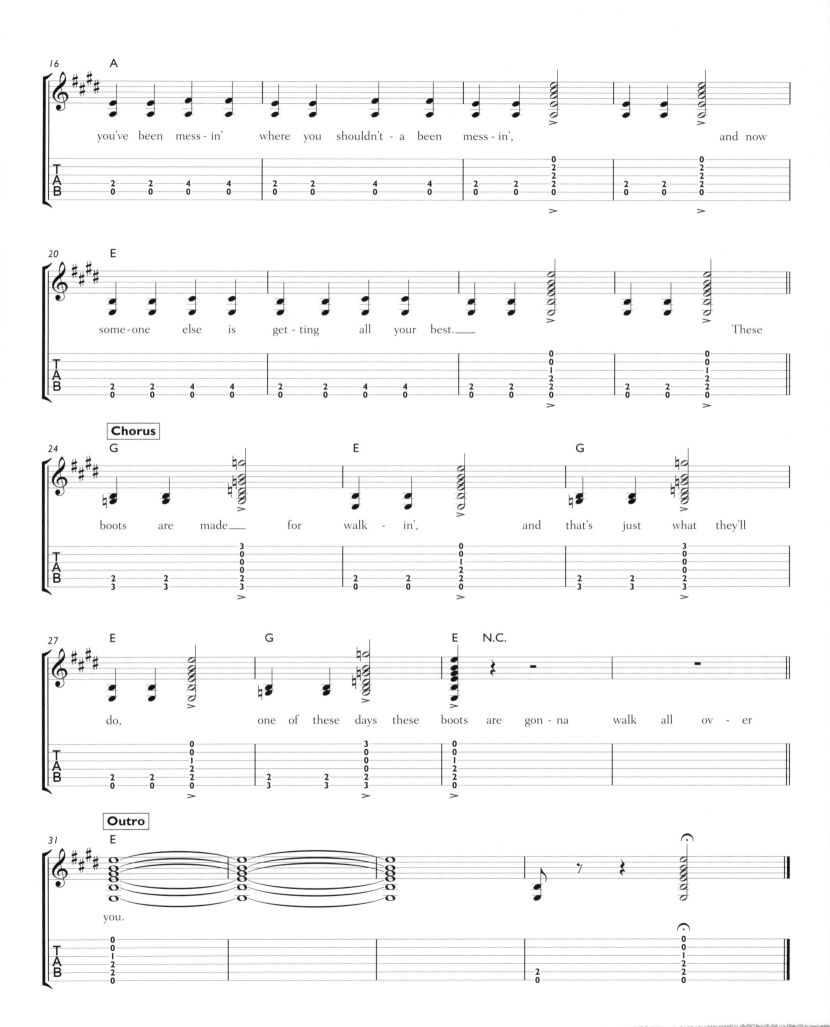

SONGS I WALK THE LINE

Johnny Cash
Words and Music by John R Cash

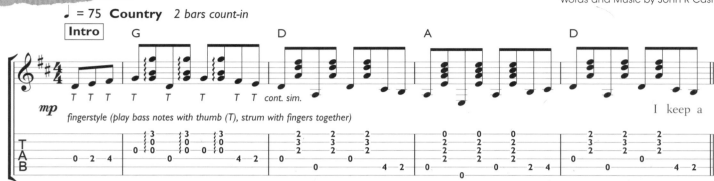

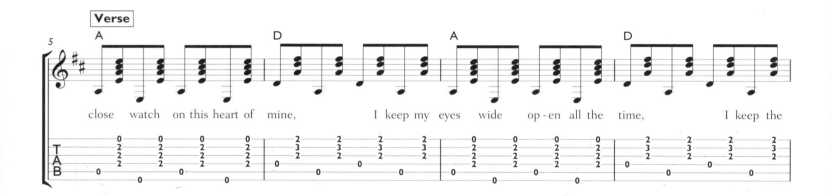

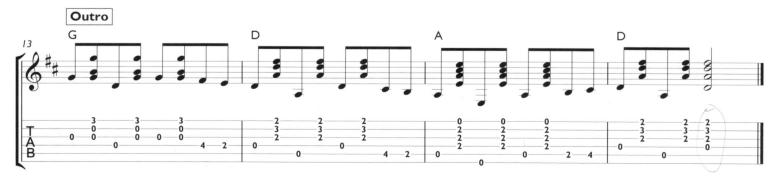

FREIGHT TRAIN

In your exam, you will be assessed on the following elements:

1 Tone quality

The guitar plays the melody in both the intro and outro. Let these melodies sing out. Aim for a full sound with a warm tone.

2 Smooth chord changes

The guitar plays a chord accompaniment in the verses, using the chords G, D^7, B^7 and C. All of these use three fingers, with the exception of B^7 which uses all four fingers. Make sure that you move smoothly from one chord to the next.

3 Strumming

The strumming patterns used in the first and second verses are slightly different.

For a more fluid effect you should use up-strums in the second verse for the chords on the second beat of the bar:

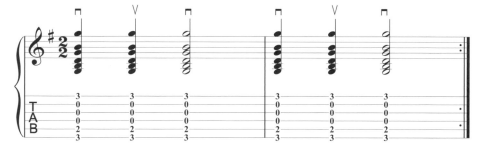

SONGS FREIGHT TRAIN

Taj Mahal
Words and Music by Paul James, Fred Williams and Elizabeth Cotten

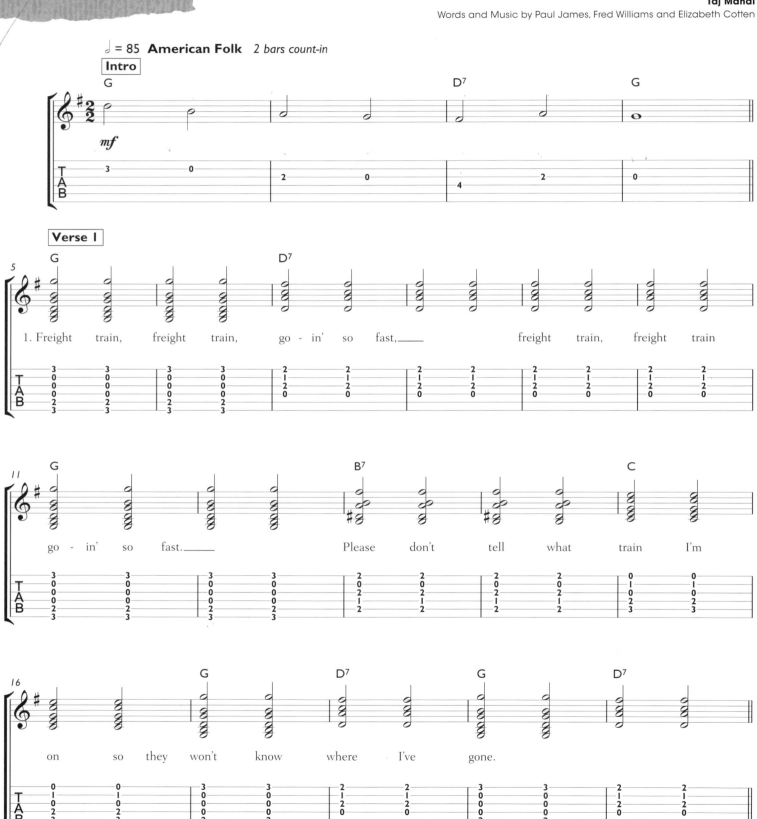

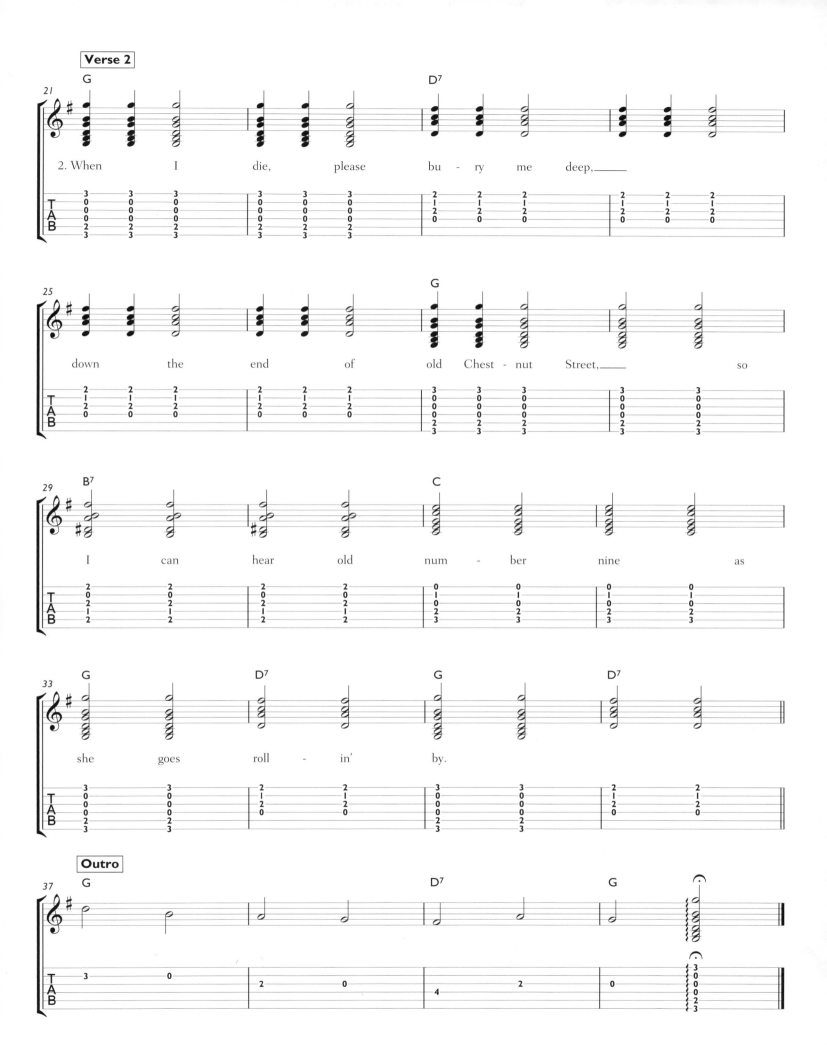

I BELIEVE I'LL DUST MY BROOM

In your exam, you will be assessed on the following technical elements:

1 Shuffle accompaniment

For most of this song, the guitar part is a 'sixth shuffle' accompaniment. The chord name (A^7, D^7, E^7) tells you which open string the pattern is based on. For A^7, the open A string underpins the 'rocking' motion between the fifth and sixth of the chord on the D string (frets 2 and 4); this idea is simply transferred to the D and G strings for D^7 and the E and A strings for E^7. Keep a steady rhythm throughout the song.

2 Tone quality

At bar 15, the guitar plays a solo based on two notes. Be careful that the A does not ring on during the rest or under the C – damp the strings to prevent this. Play out and aim for a full sound with a warm tone.

3 Stop time

Bars 23–24 only have one note per bar: an accented ♪ on the first beat. This is known as a 'stop time' section. Make these notes short and loud and make sure they are exactly in time – it is tempting to rush. Count a steady **1 2 3 4** in your head and listen out for the bass drum part which plays the same rhythm – make sure you are exactly in time with the drums.

BAND OPTION

TRACK 12 demo · TRACK 13 backing

I BELIEVE I'LL DUST MY BROOM

Words and Music by Robert Johnson

♩ = 100 **Blues** *2 bars count-in*

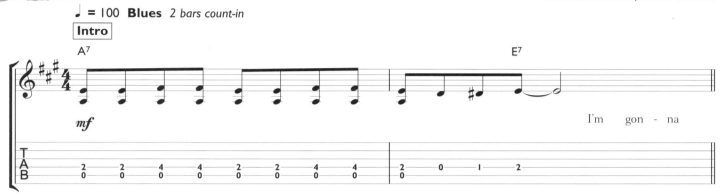

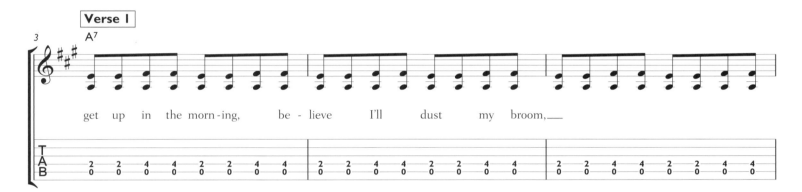

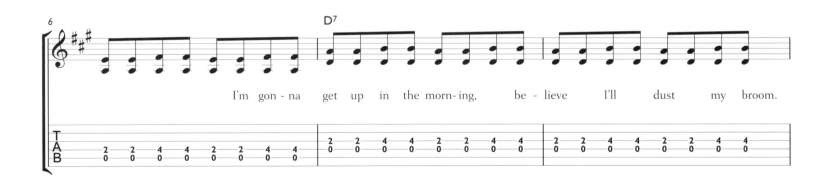

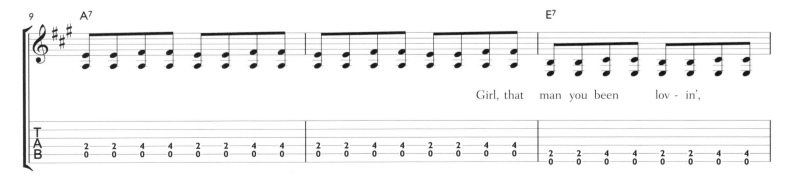

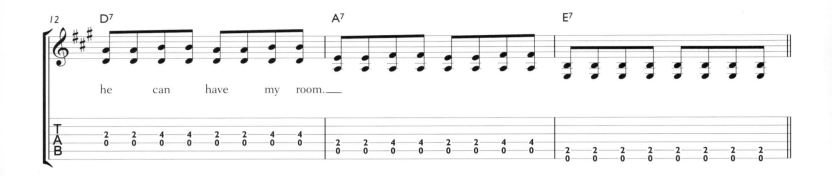

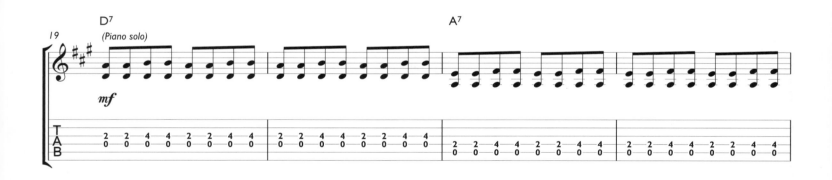

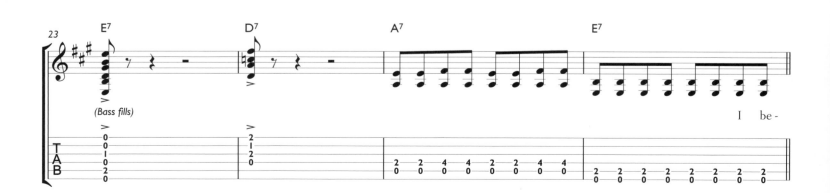

Verse 2

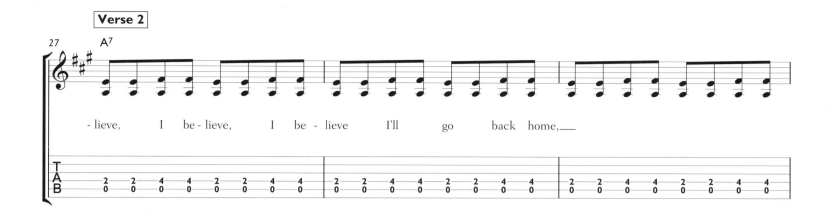

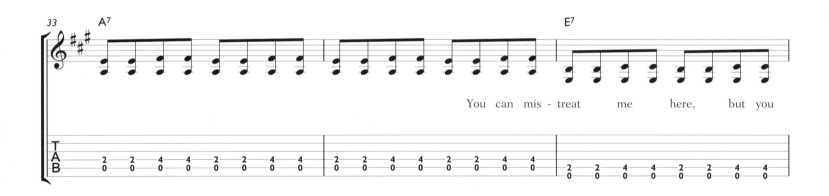

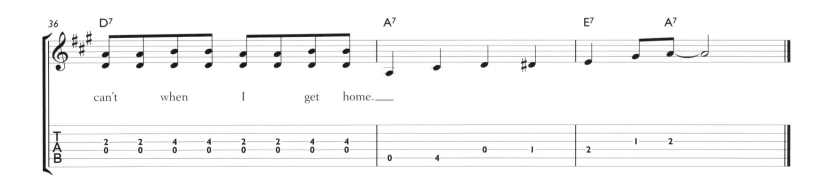

I'M GONNA BE (500 MILES)

The Proclaimers

'I'm Gonna Be (500 Miles)' was written and performed by the Scottish duo The Proclaimers – identical twins Charlie and Craig Reid. It is from *Sunshine on Leith* (1988) – an album of catchy post-punk songs about love, life and politics in Scotland.

The song did not enjoy success until it was used in the 1993 film *Benny & Joon*, when it became a worldwide hit. Since then, it has been used in advertisements, films, and on television worldwide. It is very popular in Scotland where it is played at major sporting events every time the national team scores.

This guitar part uses mainly two-note power chords (chords which contain only the root and the fifth of the chord).

Most of the ♩ notes in this song are marked *staccato*. This is shown by a dot above or below the note.

- The *staccato* ♩ notes should be cut short rather than being allowed to sound for a full beat
- Your right hand should fall back into place approximately halfway between beats, cutting off the previous chord and resting briefly before playing the next chord exactly on the beat.

The accented E major chords in the chorus provide contrast and should be allowed to ring for the full ♩. Make them louder than the *staccato* chords – this will probably happen naturally because you play all six strings for these chords.

‘I'm *gonna* be
the one who goes
along with *you*’

ABOUT THE SONGS

SHEENA IS A PUNK ROCKER

Ramones

The Ramones were an American punk band (some people say the first ever punk band) famous for their appearances at the iconic New York CBGB club. Their music is typical of punk – short energetic songs, raw and chaotic, with simple chord progressions played at breakneck speed and an impenetrable wall of sound – often with distortion and feedback and a raucous half-shouting style of singing.

'Sheena Is A Punk Rocker' is a punk rock classic. It was first released in 1977 on the album *Rocket To Russia*.

PERFORMANCE · HINTS & TIPS ·

This song is loud and energetic. It has the dynamic marking *f* at the beginning: this stands for *forte* which means play loudly.

The guitar part for 'Sheena Is A Punk Rocker' has the same rhythm of straight ♩ chords for the most of the song. Use down-strokes on the strong beats (beats 1 and 3) and up-strokes on the weaker beats (beats 2 and 4) throughout the song. This should result in fluid rhythms with maximum energy.

Make sure that you hit the last two notes of the song exactly in time – this will give the piece a really strong finish. Look out for the accents (>) and be sure that these notes are louder than the others.

'*She* had to break *away*'

THESE BOOTS ARE MADE FOR WALKIN'

Nancy Sinatra

Nancy Sinatra's recording of 'These Boots Are Made For Walkin'' was released on the album *Boots* in 1966. The song was composed by Lee Hazlewood, who wrote and produced most of her hits. A catchy pop song with defiant lyrics, it was an immediate hit in both the UK and the US.

Since then there have been many covers of the song, in a range of styles including a ska punk version by Operation Ivy and parodies both by the heavy metal band Megadeth and by Miss Piggy from the Muppets.

PERFORMANCE · HINTS & TIPS ·

This song uses a shuffle pattern on the chords E and A. It starts at bar 4, on an E chord.

- First two chords: play the open low E string and the note B (second fret on the A string) – this creates a two-note power chord (E^5). A power chord is one that only contains the root and the fifth of the chord.
- Second two chords: keep your first finger in the same place and add your third finger at the fourth fret.

For the A pattern (starting at bar 16) the same idea is simply transferred to the next pair of strings (fretted notes on the D string against the open A string).

Play using down-strokes only, and take care not to strike the higher open strings.

Make sure that the chords with accents (>) are louder than the shuffle pattern.

'Now *someone* else *is getting* all *your* best'

I WALK THE LINE

Johnny Cash

The American singer-songwriter Johnny Cash (1932–2003) was the son of a poor cotton farmer in Arkansas. He was a country-influenced singer with an unmistakable voice – a deep, distinctive bass-baritone. His songs, which he started writing when he was only 12, often use themes taken from the harsher side of life – divorce, prison, murder and war.

'I Walk The Line', his first pop (as opposed to country) hit, was originally released on Sun Records in 1956.

PERFORMANCE · HINTS & TIPS ·

'I Walk The Line' has the same guitar pattern all the way through. This type of pattern, where bass notes and strummed chords are played alternately, is often found in country music:

- the thumb plays bass notes
- the fingers are held together and strum the chords.

Some players prefer to use a plectrum for this type of pattern because it can give a clearer sound. However, you have to control the plectrum carefully and make sure that you play the correct bass notes.

The intro and outro (apart from the final chord) are just the same – so you only have to learn these four bars once.

'*I keep* my eyes *wide* open *all* the *time*'

FREIGHT TRAIN

Taj Mahal

'Freight Train' was written in the early 20th century by Elizabeth Cotten, when she was only 12 years old. She was self-taught and played the guitar left-handed, but without restringing it, so used her thumb to play the melody and fingers to play bass and harmony. She did not start recording and performing in public until she was in her sixties, but still went on to win major awards.

'Freight Train' became very popular during the American folk revival in the 1950s and 1960s, when many artists covered it, including Peter, Paul and Mary, and Joan Baez. It is now considered to be an American folk classic. This version is based on the cover by the American blues musician Taj Mahal.

In this song, the intro and the outro, apart from the final chord, are the same – so you only have to learn these four bars once.

Look out for the pause (𝄐) at the end of this song. Hold this chord on longer than two beats – try counting two beats in your head and add another beat before damping the strings.

This song is also in the keyboards, vocals, bass and drums books so you can get together and play it in a band.

'Please *don't tell* what *train* I'm on'

I BELIEVE I'LL DUST MY BROOM

Robert Johnson

'Dust My Broom' is a 12-bar blues first recorded by the Mississippi blues singer and guitarist Robert Johnson (1911–1938). Like most blues (early American black music originally performed by one singer accompanied on guitar or banjo), 'Dust My Broom' has four beats in a bar, is built on three chords and has a three-line verse where the second line is a repeat of the first.

Robert Johnson lived a short but turbulent life as a wandering musician and enjoyed little commercial success. Although he only recorded 30 songs, most of these went on to become classics and have had a great influence on many rock musicians today. Hundreds of versions of 'Dust My Broom' have been recorded, notably by Eric Clapton, Led Zeppelin, Bob Dylan, Canned Heat and Fleetwood Mac. Johnson died when he was 26 from drinking poisoned whisky.

PERFORMANCE HINTS & TIPS

There is a short guitar solo in bars 15–18; play out here. At bar 19 the piano has a solo while the guitar returns to the shuffle accompaniment. Don't play too loudly here and allow the piano to be heard.

Watch out for the accidentals. An accidental is a sharp ♯, flat ♭ or natural ♮ used during the song which is not in the key signature. 'Dust My Broom' is in the key of A and so has a key signature of three sharps. But this is a blues song and uses several blue notes – where notes of the scale are flattened. C♮ is a blue note.

This song is also in the keyboards, vocals, bass and drums books so you can get together and play it in a band.

'*I believe I'll go back home*'

SESSION SKILLS · PLAYBACK

For your exam, you can choose either Playback or Improvising (see page 26).
If you choose Playback, you will be asked to play some music you have not seen
or heard before.

In the exam, you will be given the song chart and the examiner will play a recording
of the music. You will hear several two-bar phrases on the recording: you should play
each of them straight back in turn. There's a rhythm track going throughout, which
helps you keep in time. There should not be any gaps in the music.

In the exam you will have two chances to play with the recording:
- First time – for practice
- Second time – for assessment.

You should listen to the audio, copying what you hear; you can also read the music
from the song chart. Here are some practice song charts which are also on the CD
in this book.

Don't forget that the Playback test can include requirements which may not be
shown in these examples, including those from earlier grades. Check the parameters
at www.trinityrock.com to prepare everything which might come up in your exam.

'I really *like* the *way* music *looks* on *paper.* It *looks* like *art* to *me*'

Steve Vai

Practice playback 1

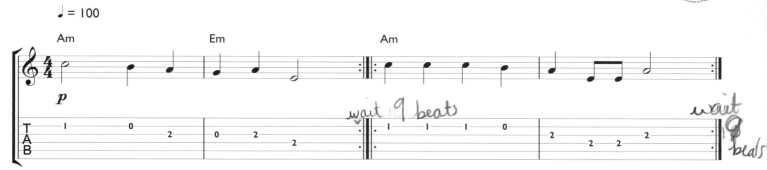

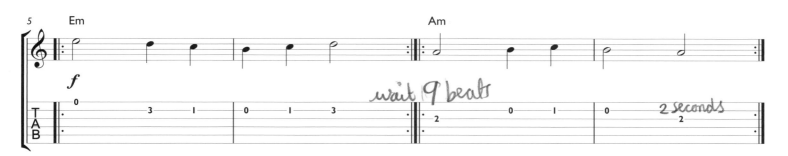

Practice playback 2

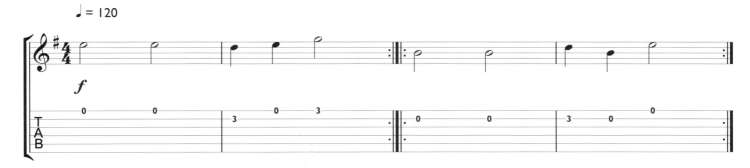

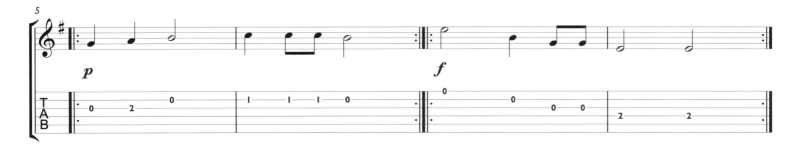

IMPROVISING

For your exam, you can choose either Playback (see page 24), or Improvising. If you choose to improvise, you will be asked to improvise over a backing track that you haven't heard before in a specified style.

In the exam, you will be given a song chart and the examiner will play a recording of the backing track. The backing track consists of a passage of music played on a loop. You can choose whether to play a lead melodic line, rhythmic chords, or a combination of the two.

In the exam you will have two chances to play with the recording:
• First time – for practice
• Second time – for assessment.

Here are some improvising charts for practice which are also on the CD in this book.

Don't forget that the Improvising test can include requirements which may not be shown in these examples, including those from earlier grades. Check the parameters at www.trinityrock.com to prepare everything which might come up in your exam.

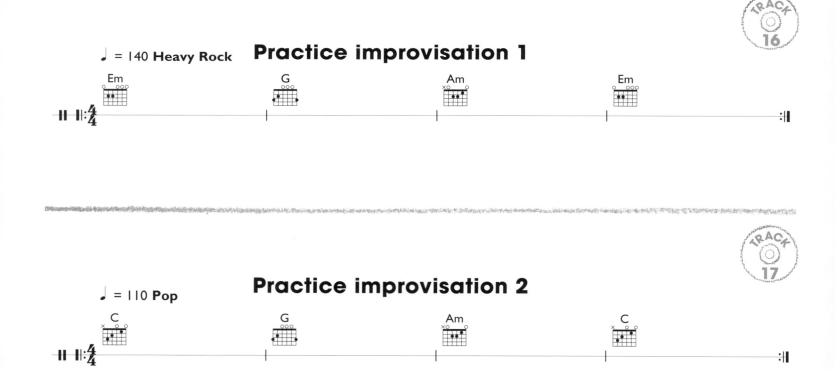

TRACK 16

♩ = 140 **Heavy Rock**   **Practice improvisation 1**

| Em | G | Am | Em |

TRACK 17

♩ = 110 **Pop**   **Practice improvisation 2**

| C | G | Am | C |

CHOOSING A SONG FOR YOUR EXAM

There are lots of options to help you choose your three songs for the exam. For Songs 1 and 2, you can choose a song which is:

- from this book
- from www.trinityrock.com

Or for Song 2 you can choose a song which is:

- sheet music from a printed or online source.
- your own arrangement of a song or a song you have written yourself (see page 28).

You can play the song unaccompanied or with a backing track (minus the solo instrument). If you like, you can create a backing track yourself (or with friends), or you could add your own vocals – or both.

For Grade 1, the song should last between one and three-and-a-half minutes, and the level of difficulty should be similar to your other songs. When choosing a song, think about:

- Does it work on my instrument?
- Are there any technical elements that are too difficult for me? (If so, perhaps save it for when you do the next grade.)
- Do I enjoy playing it?
- Does it work with my other pieces to create a good set-list?

See www.trinityrock.com for information and advice on choosing your own song.

SHEET MUSIC

You must always bring an original copy of the book or a download sheet with email certificate for each song you perform in the exam. If you choose to write your own song you must provide the examiner with a copy of the sheet music. Your music can be:

- a lead sheet with lyrics, chords and melody line
- a chord chart with lyrics
- a full score using conventional staff notation
- see page 28 for details on presenting a song you have written yourself.

The title of the song and your name should be on the sheet music.

WRITING YOUR OWN SONG

You can play a song that you have written yourself for one of the choices in your exam. For Grade 1, your song should last between one and three-and-a-half minutes, so it is likely to be quite straightforward. It is sometimes difficult to know where to begin, however. Here are some suggestions for starting points:

- **A melody**: many songs are made up around a 'hook' (a short catchy melodic idea, usually only a few notes long).
  Try writing a couple of ideas for hooks here:

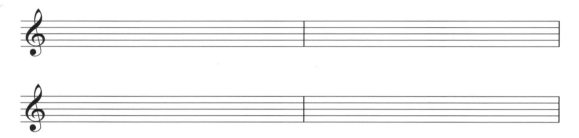

- **A chord sequence**: a short chord sequence can provide an entire verse or chorus. Write your ideas for a chord sequence here:

‖ | | | | | | | |

WRITING YOUR SONG DOWN

Rock and pop music is often written as a **lead sheet** with the lyrics (if there are any), chords and a melody line.

- As a guitar player, you may want to write your part on a **five-line stave** or as **tab**. Both have been used for the songs in this book..

- You can, if you prefer, use a **graph** or **table** to represent your music, as long as it is clear to anyone else (including the examiner) how the song goes.

- **A rhythm**: a short repeated rhythm will often underpin an entire song. Think of a couple of short rhythms you could use here:

‖——————————————————|——————————————————|

‖——————————————————|——————————————————|

There are plenty of other ways of starting: perhaps with a riff or a lyric, for example.

You will also need to consider the **structure** of your song (verse and chorus, 12-bar blues, and so on), the **style** it is in (blues, hard rock, etc.), and what **instruments** it is for (e.g. solo guitar or voice/keyboards/guitar . . .).

There are many choices to be made – which is why writing a song is such a rewarding thing to do.

PLAYING IN A BAND

Playing in a band is exciting: it can be a lot of fun and, as with everything, the more you do it, the easier it gets. It is very different from playing on your own. Everyone contributes to the overall sound: the most important skill you need to develop is listening.

For a band to sound good, the players need to be 'together' – that mainly means keeping in time with each other, but also playing at the same volume, and with the same kind of feeling.

Your relationship with the other band members is also important. Talk with them about the music you play, the music you like, and what you'd like the band to achieve short-term and long-term.

Band rehearsals are important – you should not be late, tired or distracted by your mobile phone! Being positive makes a huge difference. Try to create a friendly atmosphere in rehearsals so that everybody feels comfortable trying out new things. Don't worry about making mistakes: that is what rehearsals are for.

'Freight Train' (page 12) and 'Dust My Broom' (page 15) are arranged for band. You will find parts for vocals, keyboards, bass and drums in the other Trinity Rock & Pop Grade 1 books. Trinity offers exams for groups of musicians at various levels. The songs arranged for bands are ideal to include as part of a set-list for these exams. Have a look at the website for more details.

HINTS AND TIPS

• Plan your band practices in advance. Think about what you would like to do before you get there.

• Record your practice sessions and listen back for sections that worked well and bits that had problems.

• In some songs you will play a supporting role; at other times you may take more of a lead. In both cases you need to listen to the overall group as well as to your own part. Be aware of how you affect the overall sound.

PLAYING WITH BACKING TRACKS

The CD contains demos and backing tracks of all the songs in the book. The additional songs at www.trinityrock.com also come with demos and backing tracks.

- In your exam, you should play with the backing track, or you can create your own (see below).
- The backing tracks start with a click track, which sets the tempo and helps you start accurately.
- Be careful to set the balance between the volume of the backing track and your instrument.
- Listen carefully to the backing track to ensure you are playing in time.

If you are creating your own backing track here are some further tips:
- Make sure the sound quality is of a good standard.
- Think carefully about the instruments/sounds you are putting on the backing track.
- Avoid copying what you are playing on the backing track – it should support not duplicate.
- Do you need to include a click track at the beginning?

COPYRIGHT IN A SONG

If you are a singer or songwriter it is important to know about copyright. When someone writes a song or creates an arrangement they own the copyright (sometimes called 'the rights') to that version. The copyright means that other people cannot copy it, sell it, perform it in a concert, make it available online or record it without the owner's permission or the appropriate licence. When you write a song you automatically own the copyright to it, which means that other people cannot copy your work. But just as importantly, you cannot copy other people's work, or perform it in public without their permission or the appropriate licence.

Points to remember
- You can create a cover version of a song for an exam or other non-public performance.
- You cannot record your cover version and make your recording available to others (by copying it or uploading it to a website) without the appropriate licence.
- You own the copyright of your own original song, which means that no one is allowed to copy it.
- You cannot copy someone else's song without their permission or the appropriate licence.
- If you would like to use somebody else's words in your own song you must check if they are in copyright and, if so, we recommend you confirm with the author that they are happy for the words to be used as lyrics.
- Materials protected by copyright can normally be used as lyrics in our examinations as these are private performances under copyright law. The examiner may ask you the name of the original author in the exam.
- When you present your own song to the examiner make sure you include the title, the names of any writers and the source of your lyrics.

YOUR PAGE

NOTES

ALSO AVAILABLE

Trinity College London Rock & Pop examinations 2012-2017 are also available for:

Bass Initial
ISBN: 978-0-85736-227-8

Bass Grade 1
ISBN: 978-0-85736-228-5

Bass Grade 2
ISBN: 978-0-85736-229-2

Bass Grade 3
ISBN: 978-0-85736-230-8

Bass Grade 4
ISBN: 978-0-85736-231-5

Bass Grade 5
ISBN: 978-0-85736-232-2

Bass Grade 6
ISBN: 978-0-85736-233-9

Bass Grade 7
ISBN: 978-0-85736-234-6

Bass Grade 8
ISBN: 978-0-85736-235-3

Keyboards Initial
ISBN: 978-0-85736-236-0

Keyboards Grade 1
ISBN: 978-0-85736-237-7

Keyboards Grade 2
ISBN: 978-0-85736-238-4

Keyboards Grade 3
ISBN: 978-0-85736-239-1

Keyboards Grade 4
ISBN: 978-0-85736-240-7

Keyboards Grade 5
ISBN: 978-0-85736-241-4

Keyboards Grade 6
ISBN: 978-0-85736-242-1

Keyboards Grade 7
ISBN: 978-0-85736-243-8

Keyboards Grade 8
ISBN: 978-0-85736-244-5

Drums Initial
ISBN: 978-0-85736-245-2

Drums Grade 1
ISBN: 978-0-85736-246-9

Drums Grade 2
ISBN: 978-0-85736-247-6

Drums Grade 3
ISBN: 978-0-85736-248-3

Drums Grade 4
ISBN: 978-0-85736-249-0

Drums Grade 5
ISBN: 978-0-85736-250-6

Drums Grade 6
ISBN: 978-0-85736-251-3

Drums Grade 7
ISBN: 978-0-85736-252-0

Drums Grade 8
ISBN: 978-0-85736-253-7

Vocals Initial
ISBN: 978-0-85736-254-4

Vocals Grade 1
ISBN: 978-0-85736-255-1

Vocals Grade 2
ISBN: 978-0-85736-256-8

Vocals Grade 3
ISBN: 978-0-85736-257-5

Vocals Grade 4
ISBN: 978-0-85736-258-2

Vocals Grade 5
ISBN: 978-0-85736-259-9

Vocals Grade 6 (female voice)
ISBN: 978-0-85736-263-6

Vocals Grade 6 (male voice)
ISBN: 978-0-85736-260-5

Vocals Grade 7 (female voice)
ISBN: 978-0-85736-264-3

Vocals Grade 7 (male voice)
ISBN: 978-0-85736-261-2

Vocals Grade 8 (female voice)
ISBN: 978-0-85736-265-0

Vocals Grade 8 (male voice)
ISBN: 978-0-85736-262-9

Guitar Initial
ISBN: 978-0-85736-218-6

Guitar Grade 1
ISBN: 978-0-85736-219-3

Guitar Grade 2
ISBN: 978-0-85736-220-9

Guitar Grade 3
ISBN: 978-0-85736-221-6

Guitar Grade 4
ISBN: 978-0-85736-222-3

Guitar Grade 5
ISBN: 978-0-85736-223-0

Guitar Grade 6
ISBN: 978-0-85736-224-7

Guitar Grade 7
ISBN: 978-0-85736-225-4

Guitar Grade 8
ISBN: 978-0-85736-226-1